YOU'RE REA[DING]
THE WRONG [WAY]

Dr. STONE

reads from right to left, starting in the upper-right corner. Japanese is read from right to left, meaning that action, sound effects and word-balloon order are completely reversed from English order.

DEMON SLAYER

KIMETSU NO YAIBA

Story and Art by
KOYOHARU GOTOUGE

In Taisho-era Japan, kindhearted Tanjiro Kamado makes a living selling charcoal. But his peaceful life is shattered when a demon slaughters his entire family. His little sister Nezuko is the only survivor, but she has been transformed into a demon herself! Tanjiro sets out on a dangerous journey to find a way to return his sister to normal and destroy the demon who ruined his life.

DEMON SLAYER

KIMETSU NO YAIBA

1

Story and Art by
KOYOHARU GOTOUGE

RATED
T
TEEN

VIZ

SOMETIMES THOSE WITHOUT A LEGAL WAY TO APPLY THEIR QUIRKS...

...FIND A WAY AROUND THE RULES.

MY HERO ACADEMIA VIGILANTES

In a superpowered society, there is nothing ordinary about evil anymore. Heroes, trained and licensed to protect and defend the public against supervillains, stand above all the rest. Not everyone can be a hero, however, and there are those who would use their powers to serve the people without legal sanction. But do they fight for justice in the shadows, or for reasons known only to themselves? Whatever they fight for, they are called... Vigilantes.

MECHA SENKU Q&A

SEARCH

Question Corner

What sort of magic can Gen do?

M.M. from Tokyo **SEARCH**

- **Mentalist card-guessing (fake)**
- **Mentalist birthday-guessing (fake)**
- **Fake fortune-telling**
- **Coin tricks**
- **Vanishing act**
- **Vocal mimicry**

AND MORE!

Science Questions	How does one make gasoline out of plastic bottle caps?
Character Questions	If Taiju and Tsukasa really fought, who would win?
Questions That Aren't Really Questions	I wanna get petrified and challenge myself to count the seconds..

Now accepting any and all queries! Submit ten billion questions to me!

My name is MECHA SENKU!!

WHRRR KLANG

Dr.STONE

...AT THAT!

LOOK...

ROCKED

HE EVEN KNOWS ABOUT THIS?! NOOO!!

A MAGNET.

WELL, SENKU?! WHADDYA THINK OF MY INVENTION?!

WITHOUT THESE IRON TOOLS WE FORGED...

...A JOB LIKE THIS WOULD'VE BEEN A CHORE AND A HALF.

OHO! THESE HERE SCIENCE BLADES ARE GREAT!

AND SO'M I.

GET READY TO BE WOWED, FOLKS!!

THIS IS REVENGE FOR ROCKING MY WORLD WITH THE MAGNET!

GAH! OF COURSE HE ALREADY KNEW!!

A WATER-WHEEL?

ROCKED ROCKED

YOU DID GOOD COMING UP WITH THIS FROM SCRATCH!

NAH, I'M PLENTY WOWED. REALLY!

YEAH, LET'S JUST GO WITH WATER-WHEEL.

"THE CONTRAPTION THAT KEEPS THE COTTON CANDY COMING"!

I EVEN HAD A NAME PREPARED.

SINCE THE GROWN-UPS ARE ALL BUSY GETTING READY FOR WINTER...

...SUIKA AND THE OTHER KIDS CAN HELP OUT!

TWIST

YAYYYY!

TOOK THREE WHOLE DAYS...

...AND NIGHTS!

IT'S...

IT'S DONE, SENKU.

CHEEP

CHEEP

Heh
Heh

BESIDES, YOU BUNCH WON'T HAVE TIME TO THINK ABOUT HIM...

...CUZ I'VE GOT A HELLISH TASK IN STORE FOR EVERY ONE OF YOU.

SOME SCHEME, PROBABLY. LEAVE HIM BE.

HRM... WHAT'S CHROME UP TO NOW?

YOU'RE GONNA BRAID THESE STRINGS OF GOLD...

...INTO SUPER-THIN GOLD WIRE!

TWIST

TWIST

THE RULES SAY YOU HAVE TO LET LITTLE SCAMPS CARRY OUT THEIR PRANKS WITHOUT SPOILING THE SURPRISE.

OH. RIGHT. ABOUT FROM HERE...

HMPH... AND JUST HOW LONG A WIRE DO WE NEED?

A MASSIVE WORKFORCE SAVES THE DAY, ONCE AGAIN.

IT'S A GOOD THING YOU BECAME CHIEF OF THIS PLACE, DEAR SENKU...

WHUUUT?

...TO THAT MOUNTAIN.

OHHH, HERE WE GO!

BAAAAD!

I'VE SEEN THE LIGHT!!

SPINNING, SPINNING...

ROLLING ALONG?

PUSHING ON.

ONE DIRECTION? ALL DAY...?

DING!

BURST

Psst   Psst

JUST TRUST ME!

WHERE ARE WE OFF TO?!

DRAG

DRAG

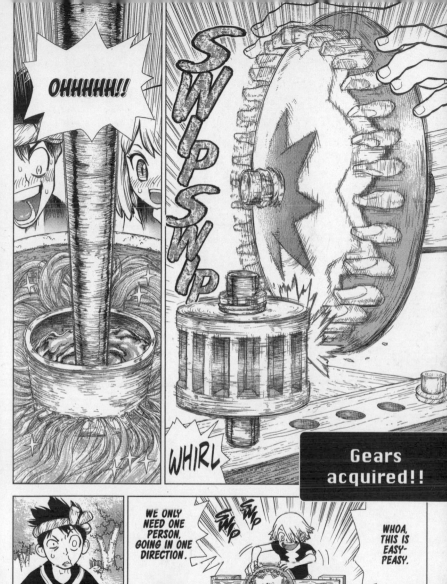

OHHHHH!!

SWIP SWIP

WHIRL

Gears acquired!!

WE ONLY NEED ONE PERSON, GOING IN ONE DIRECTION.

ROLLING ALONG LIKE THIS, I COULD DO THIS ALL DAY!

WHOA, THIS IS EASY-PEASY.

IT'S JUST A SILLY OLD TREASURE... THAT'S ALL.

OH, I DON'T MIND... REALLY.

GLANCE GLANCE

HAH! IT'S REALLY UP TO MY DARLING KOHAKU!

CLUTCH

HA HA HA HA

DADDY.

HA HA HA

GASP

I DON'T CARE.

SHOCK

MERCILESS!!

UTILITY IS KING.

SHOCK

WE'RE MAKING GEARS!

PART OF HUMANITY'S ENERGY REVOLUTION...

OHO! USING THAT, ARE WE??

...THAT HE GAVE TO KOHAKU AS A GIFT?

YOU MEAN... THE CHIEF'S HARD-WON PRIZE...

THE TEN BILLION PERCENT IDEAL RESOURCE FOR A GOOD GEAR.

OOH! KOHAKU'S SHIELD IS PERFECT FOR THIS.

YAP

ALL YOU GOTTA DO IS SPIN A CRANK!

THEN HOW ABOUT MAKING IT LIKE THAT GENERATOR THERE?!

NOT ENOUGH SPEED.

HAH! WE JUST NEED TO PUT OUR BACKS INTO IT, AND IF WE ALL SWITCH OFF...

OH, BUT WHAT ABOUT A REALLY, REALLY LONG ROPE?

YAP

LIKE, ONE KILOMETER LONG?

YOU TRYING TO KILL US?!

YAP

AND THERE IT IS. ALAS, WE HAVE NO REVIVAL FLUID WITH WHICH TO INCREASE OUR NUMBERS.

WE CAN'T HAVE SO MANY OF THE VILLAGERS DOING SCIENCE STUFF WHEN WE NEED TO STOCK UP FOR WINTER.

ALL THIS LABOR IS A PROBLEM.

...BUT I BET OUR MASTER CRAFTSMAN KASEKI IS UP TO THE TASK!

IT'LL TAKE SOME TIME AND EFFORT...

HEH HEH HEH... IN THAT CASE, WE JUST GOTTA MAKE SOMETHING ELSE.

THERE!!

SWIP
SWIP

WHIRL

WHIRL

STIR
STIR

CAN'T YOU TWO JUST DO IT SMOOTHER, WITHOUT SLOWING?!

USE YOUR SPECIAL BROTHERLY BOND!

YOU'RE ASKING THE IMPOSSIBLE...

...IT SLOWS DOWN.

HENCE THE INCONSISTENT TEXTURE.

YEAH. RIGHT WHEN THE SPIN DIRECTION REVERSES...

DID IT SHOW UP IN THE 100 TALES, PERHAPS?

THESE PEOPLE KNOW THE TERM NORI-TSUKKOMI?

YOU CAN BLAME MY DUMB OLD DAD, THEN.

AS IF!!

I GOT SWEPT UP RIGHT INTO A NORI-TSUKKOMI SKETCH COMEDY BIT, BUT...

...WHO THE HECK CARES ABOUT FLAVOR HARMONY IN COTTON CANDY?!

~NORI-TSUKKOMI: PLAYING YOUR OWN STRAIGHT MAN

TSUKASA'S ARMY'S GONNA SHOW UP BEFORE WE FINISH MAKING CELL PHONES!

WHY'RE WE GOOFING AROUND IF THERE'S THIS BIG TIME LIMIT?

REALLY? THE DEBATE OVER COTTON CANDY QUALITY?

HEH HEH HEH... CALM DOWN. BESIDES, THIS IS ACTUALLY A SERIOUS ISSUE.

...WILL BE TOO, RIGHT?

...THEN THE GOLD WIRE...

BECAUSE IF THE COTTON CANDY IS LUMPY AND INCONSISTENT...

BAAAD STUFF! GOOD THING WE TESTED WITH COTTON CANDY FIRST!

YUP. BEFORE WE GO ALL IN WITH THE GOLD...

...WE GOTTA FIGURE OUT WHAT'S WRONG.

I'M PLENTY USED TO THIS SORT OF TRIAL AND ERROR.

WHIRR

WHIRR

THIS... THIS COTTON CANDY...

I'LL TRY HARDER NEXT TIME, I SWEAR!

UGH...

...REVEALS A DISHARMONY WITH THE FLAVOR!

THIS INCONSISTENCY IN THE FIBERS...

...AND YET IT HAS A GRANULAR TEXTURE TO IT.

FLUFFY ENOUGH TO MELT ON THE TONGUE...

AGREED!

GIN

Z=52: Age of Energy

TAIJU AND YUZURIHA...

SHALL WE LET THEM ROAM FREE?

KEEP AN EYE ON THEM.

I'M NOT WORRIED.

TO THE ENEMY, THOSE TWO ARE POTENTIAL HOSTAGES. THEY WON'T HURT 'EM.

WON'T THEY BE KILLED?!

ARE TAIJU AND YUZURIHA GONNA LAST THAT LONG?

THOUGH IT'S NOT AS IF WE CAN COMMUNICATE, EITHER, SO...

I'VE SET HOMURA TO KEEP WATCH.

...ANY INTEL WILL COME WITH A TIME LAG...

FSHHH

NO. WHAT CONCERNS ME MORE...

...IS A PREEMPTIVE ATTACK BY SENKU.

BUT OTHERWISE, DON'T TREAT THEM ANY DIFFERENTLY.

WE DON'T WANT THEM LEARNING THAT SENKU IS ALIVE.

EVEN IF THEY ARE MOLES...

...IN THIS WORLD, THEY HAVE NO WAY TO COMMUNICATE WITH THEIR ALLY.

WE NEED TO STOCK UP FOR WINTER.

THAT WILL TAKE UP A LOT OF MANPOWER.

WHOOSH

...AND IF THEY BOLSTER THEIR DEFENSES, WE WON'T HAVE AN EASY TIME ATTACKING.

IN WINTER, THEY'LL BE PROTECTED BY THE FROZEN LAKE...

SENKU'S KINGDOM OF SCIENCE IS A FLOATING FORTRESS.

WE AREN'T PREPARED FOR EXTENDED SIEGE WARFARE, LOGISTICALLY.

WHICH IS WHY WE'LL END THIS...

...JUST AFTER WINTER ENDS!!

WHOOSH

...A FEW MONTHS!!

WE'VE ONLY GOT...

BAM

E=mc²

Z=52: Age of Energy

WHIP

WHIP

WHAT'S YOUR TAKE, MENTALIST?

THAT'S WHEN TSUKASA'S GONNA MAKE HIS ALL-OUT ATTACK.

HOW DO YOU KNOW?

HM... I'LL JUST TRY THINKING LIKE DEAR TSUKASA, THEN...

BUT SENKU IS NO ORDINARY FOE.

WE CONTROL THE REVIVAL FLUID...

GIVE HIM TOO MUCH TIME, AND HE'LL START PRODUCING GUNPOWDER AGAIN.

...SO OUR STRENGTH ONLY GROWS AS TIME PASSES.

THAT IMPRESSION'S A LITTLE TOO GOOD...

SWEET...

UNTHINK-
ABLE.

NO.

JUST ONE
LICK?

COULD
KILL ME.

BUT
THAT'S
NOT ALL
IT IS...

THERE'S A
STRATEGIC
ELEMENT
TO THIS.

WE SAW
THAT THIS
SENTIMENTAL
BUNCH...

...WOULDN'T
ABANDON
A SINGLE
SENTRY.

SINCE WE
WENT TO
THE TROUBLE
ANYWAY, IN
THE SPIRIT
OF SHARING...

...WHY
NOT...

...GIVE SOME
TO THAT GIRL,
ALL ALONE
OUT THERE?
THAT'S HOW
I SAW IT.

LIKE I'D EAT THIS.

IDIOT.

BUT JUST TO BE SAFE, YOU COULD FEED HALF OF IT TO SOME ANIMALS.

DON'T WORRY. IT'S NOT POISON.

SENKU

Don't worry.
It's not poison.
But just to be
safe, you could
half of it

...

IT MIGHT JUST GET SOME OF THEM TO SWITCH SIDES.

HEH HEH HEH... SWEETS ARE A POWERFUL INCENTIVE.

IF THIS HOMURA IS MONITORING US, WORD OF OUR COTTON CANDY SHOULD REACH THE TSUKASA EMPIRE.

NOD NOD

AS UNDERHANDED AS EVER. I'M IN AWE, ACTUALLY.

OH, I SEE.

TOK

TOK

TOK

COTTON CANDY!

...?!

SENKU

COTTON CANDY

THAT WAY THEY'D BE ABLE TO CHASE US DOWN IF THE WHOLE VILLAGE DECIDED TO MAKE A RUN FOR IT.

AND SHE'LL BE CLOSE ENOUGH TO KNOW RIGHT AWAY IF WE START TO MOBILIZE IN A BIG WAY.

ACK! SHE'S WATCHING US? EVEN NOW?!

I WOULDN'T BE SURPRISED.

THERE ISN'T A SINGLE PERSON IN THIS VILLAGE WHO WOULD ENTERTAIN SUCH COWARDLY THOUGHTS!

HAH! ABANDON OUR ELDERS? BE ON THE RUN FOR THE REST OF OUR DAYS?

NOPE. NOBODY. DEFINITELY NOT.

AND WE'VE GOT OLD FOLKS WHO PROBABLY COULDN'T MAKE THE TRIP.

RELOCATING WOULD BE HARD, SINCE WE NEED TO START STOCKING UP FOR WINTER SOON.

EEP... RUNNING AWAY WITH EVERYONE WAS MY PLAN B IF THINGS GOT BAD.

CHATTER

CHATTER

SO I VERY MUCH DOUBT SHE'LL CAUSE US ANY TROUBLE.

AT THE SAME TIME, WINNING HER OVER TO OUR SIDE IS OPELESS-HAY.

DEAR HOMURA HAS THE UTMOST RESPECT FOR HYOGA, THOUGH.

IF HIS ORDER WAS TO MONITOR US, SHE'S THE TYPE TO OBEY.

WHAT SORT OF WOMAN IS HOMURA?

...

GEN.

WE REALLY OUGHT TO BE GRATEFUL TO DEAR HOMURA.

HER FIRES GAVE US JUST THE INGREDIENT WE NEEDED FOR THIS.

YOU PEOPLE DON'T KNOW SENKU AT ALL.

NO. PRETTY SURE THAT'S NOT THE CASE.

GUESS THAT FIERY GIRL'S YOUR TYPE, THEN??

WHAAAT? IS OLD SENKU FINALLY SHOWING SOME INTEREST IN A LADY?!

TOK
TOK

NO DOUBT. SHE'S THE ONLY ONE HYOGA TRUSTS TO BEGIN WITH.

$E=mc^2$

I BET HOMURA'S KEEPING...

...AN EYE ON US.

A TASTE TEST... ERM, I MEAN...

A TRIAL RUN, YES!!

MAKES SENSE.

!!

...WITH COTTON CANDY!

...A TRIAL RUN...

WE SHOULD DO...

Can...

...dy

...ton

Cot...

...AND RUINED ALL OUR YAM LIQUOR. EVEN THE MIRIN, AND THAT'S NOT REALLY BOOZE.

THAT HOMURA WOMAN, WITH THE ENEMY... SHE SET ALL THEM FIRES...

BUT WHAT HAPPENS IF WE TOSS IN GOLD, INSTEAD?

YOU SPIN IT AROUND, AND THE CENTRIFUGAL FORCE PUSHES THIN STRINGS OF SUGAR OUT THE HOLES.

BASICALLY, IT'S A CONTRAPTION FOR MAKING COTTON CANDY.

SNIP SNIP

GREAT! TIME TO PUT MY GOLD TO USE!

AH... PERFECT FOR WIRING IN ELECTRONICS, YES?

THIS CONVERSATION'S IQ JUMPED BACK UP AGAIN.

HEH HEH HEH... BINGO! TEN BILLION POINTS FOR YOU.

WE GET ULTRA-THIN GOLD WIRE!

HANG ON! GOLD'S A PRECIOUS COMMODITY, SO WE CAN'T AFFORD TO MESS UP.

SCAMPER

E=mc

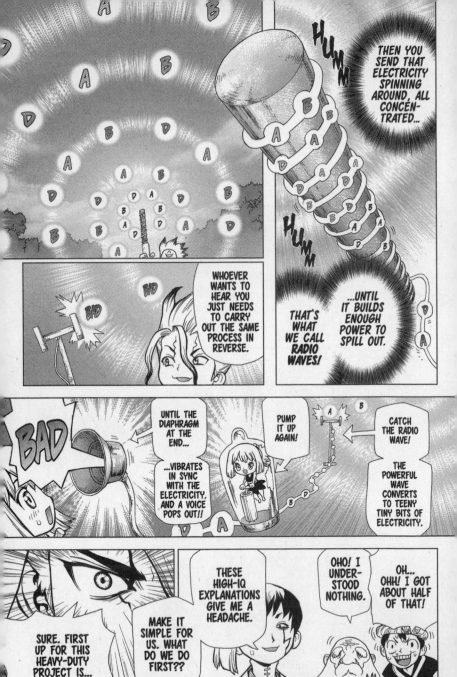

MOSTLY CUZ THERE'RE SO MANY MATERIALS WE GOTTA GET FIRST!

...IS A JUMBO-SIZED, HEAVY-DUTY PROJECT.

BECAUSE MAKING A CELL PHONE IN THIS STONE WORLD...

BACK UP!!

BA...

YOU TWO NEED TO TAKE IT DOWN A NOTCH.

MIND EXPLAINING HOW IT WORKS IN SIMPLE TERMS, BOY?!

PUFF   PUFF

RIGHT, SO, ABOUT THESE CELL PHONES!

YOU CAN TALK TO PEOPLE WHO'RE CRAZY FAR AWAY FROM YOU? TOO FREAKING COOL!!

...AND SHOOTS SOME TEENY TINY BURSTS OF ELECTRICITY DOWN THE LINE.

...IT SYNCS UP WITH THE VIBRATIONS...

WHEN YOU AIM THOSE VIBRATIONS INTO A DIAPHRAGM...

ANYHOO... OUR VOICES ARE JUST VIBRATIONS IN THE AIR.

That's where the vacuum tubes come in.

...WE PUMP 'EM UP LIKE CRAZY!

BUT SINCE THEY'RE SO TEENY TINY...

BW OO OM

Z=51: Sweets for the Stone World

...

FIRE...

FORGING...?

IT'S ALL THANKS TO SENKU WINNING THE CHIEF'S THRONE! THE SPOILS OF WAR!!

SURE IS EASIER WHEN THE WHOLE VILLAGE HELPS OUT!

YUP. REALLY APPRECIATE IT.

MECHA SENKU Q&A **SEARCH** Question Corner

I'm a dog person, so I felt so bad for the dog in volume 1 whose owner was petrified. What ended up happening to that pup?

Today's Pupper from Akita Prefecture SEARCH

The little guy hung in there and stuck with his owner for a while, but...in order to survive, it eventually tapped into its wild instincts!

Dogs in similar situations form a pack, couple up and begin breeding. That original dog never forgot its owner, but he did what it took to survive!

Perhaps the descendants of that dog are still around, 3,700 years later!

WE CAN DO IT!

OHO!!

I MEAN, THOSE SULFA DRUGS SEEMED BAAAD AT FIRST, BUT WE MADE THAT HAPPEN, RIGHT?

YOU PEOPLE PROBABLY AREN'T AWARE, SO LET ME JUST SAY...

NOTHING UNTHINKABLE ABOUT IT.

PLASTIC, HE SAYS? REALLY?

...THIS ROAD MAP IS CHOCK-FULL OF UNTHINKABLE THINGS!

...WE'RE TEN BILLION PERCENT BOUND TO REACH THAT GOAL IF WE JUST FOLLOW THE STEPS.

NO MATTER HOW FAR-OFF SOMETHING SEEMS...

THAT'S HOW SCIENCE WORKS!!

WINE

MERCURY

VACUUM PUMP

ROCHELLE SALT

LIGHT BULB

PHOSPHORUS

HEAD-PHONES

MIC

VACUUM TUBE

GOAL!

CELL PHONE

TAIJU AND YUZU-RIHA!!

WE'VE GOT TWO MOLES!

MAKE SMART-PHONES, HUH?

SMART-PHONES...?

THAT'D BE NICE! I'D KILL FOR A SMART-PHONE, YEAH!

SMART-PHONES?!

HEH HEH HEH... THAT LUNKHEAD TAIJU WANTED A SMARTPHONE SO BADLY.

AND NOW IT'S ABOUT TO BECOME REALITY.

WELL, PHONES, ANYWAY! MINUS THE SMART PART!!

CHATTER
CHATTER

BAAAD! I WANNA KNOW...

...HOW IT WORKS!!

HOW COULD SUCH A THING EVER EXIST...?

SOUNDS LIKE SORCERY TO ME!!

GRUMBLE

BUT WHO'S OUR MOLE...?

SURE!

THESE ARE WEAPONS?

ALREADY TAKEN CARE OF.

SAY YOU SEND A MOLE INTO THE ENEMY CAMP—THEY CAN FEED YOU INTEL IN REAL TIME, LEADING TO ULTIMATE VICTORY!!

GOOD COMMUNICATION CAN TURN THE TIDE OF ANY BATTLE!

IF WE COORDINATE THIS RIGHT, WE COULD TAKE DOWN THE TSUKASA EMPIRE WITHOUT SPILLING A DROP OF BLOOD!

And YY just went to the bathroom alone!

XX is light on defense now.

...BUT WE AIN'T REVIVING A SINGLE STONE STATUE AROUND HERE.

THE REVIVAL FLUID RECIPE ITSELF IS SIMPLE ENOUGH...

...BUT WE'D NEED A TON OF BOTH, AND EVEN MORE TIME.

IT'S POSSIBLE, IN THEORY, TO MAKE IT FROM POOP AND SEASHELLS...

WE DON'T HAVE ANY *NITRIC ACID.*

ALL THIS SCIENCE TALK ISN'T HELPING ME SEE THE BIG PICTURE.

EXPLAIN IT TO US NICE AND SIMPLE, OKAY?

SENKU ONLY HAD A HANDFUL OF GUNPOWDER REMAINING.

HEH HEH HEH... AND EVEN THAT HANDFUL'S ALL GONE NOW!

WITHOUT NITRIC ACID, WE CAN'T MAKE ANY MORE GUNPOWDER EITHER.

GOOD OLD TSUKASA WILL HAVE ALREADY PUT TWO AND TWO TOGETHER.

GEN'S REPORT WAS NOTHING BUT LIES.

TMP TMP TMP TMP TMP

THE VILLAGE IN QUESTION...

...IS ALREADY ARMED WITH INCREDIBLE SCIENTIFIC MIGHT.

YOUR SENKU!

AND HE'S ALIVE...

BUT WE'RE ALL HAPPY HERE!

HA HA! THOUGH, EVEN BACK IN THE DAY, I WAS ALREADY A BIG FAN OF TSUKASA HERE, MR. STRONGEST PRIMATE!!

AND WHEN A STRONG, HANDSOME GUY IS ARMED WITH A CONVINCING ARGUMENT LIKE THAT...

...BREAKING DOWN HIS SUPPORTERS WITH CLEVER WORDS ALONE IS NIGH IMPOSSIBLE...

YES. EVEN IN THE PAST WORLD, TSUKASA WAS A CHARISMATIC FELLOW.

WELL, HYOGA?

DID YOU THINK THE WORLD 3,700 YEARS AGO WAS A PARADISE?

NO.

BUT FROM THE MOMENT WE WERE BORN, BACK IN OUR TIME, WE WERE TOLD...

HYOGA...

BEHOLD NATURE'S BOUNTY.

"EVERY LAST INCH OF THIS WORLD BELONGS TO ONE GREEDY OLD BASTARD OR ANOTHER."

THIS IS THE SAME WORLD THAT BIRTHED HUMANS EONS AGO.

WE LACK FOR NOTHING.

IT BELONGS TO NO ONE.

IN THAT OLD WORLD, PEOPLE PILLAGED AND WAGED WAR.

THE HAVES GORGED THEMSELVES ON US YOUNG HAVE-NOTS.

HALF OF WHAT WE EARNED WENT INTO PAYING RENT... WE WERE BASICALLY SLAVES, IF YOU THINK ABOUT IT.

AIN'T THAT THE TRUTH! WE ALL HAD TO WORK OUR BUTTS OFF.

Z=50: Humanity's Greatest Weapon

MECHA SENKU Q&A

SEARCH — Question Corner

It looks like Suika's helmet changed!
Is it a different breed of plant?

K.N. from Nagasaki Prefecture **SEARCH**

Old | New

The first one was destroyed by Magma during the Grand Bout.

That's why Senku and Kaseki made Suika a brand-new helmet! For just that reason.

I KNEW YOU'D DO THE RIGHT THING LIKE A GOOD BOY!

THAT EARNEST-NESS IS GONNA GET YOU KILLED SOMEDAY...

KINRO!!

The curled-up leaf on top is key! When she aims it at a target, it acts as a *parabolic reflector*, meaning she'll be ten billion percent sure to eavesdrop on even whispered conversations. The perfect ability for *Great Detective Suika!!*

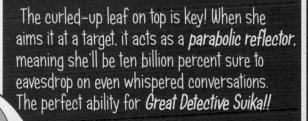

THIS IS A TOTAL VICTORY FOR ISHIGAMI VILLAGE!!

AND WE WARDED OFF THE ATTACK WITHOUT LOSING A SINGLE ONE OF OUR OWN.

OUR HOMES CAN BE REBUILT!

YEAHHHHHH

ARE WE JUST GOING TO SIT BACK AND WAIT?!

NO.

BUT NOW DEAR TSUKASA WILL LEAD THE CHARGE HIMSELF.

HIM AND HIS ENTIRE ARMY, I'M AFRAID...

YOU HAD US WORRIED THERE...

THIS WAS YOUR VICTORY, SUIKA!

...WITH A PARTICULARLY FUN SCIENTIFIC INVENTION!

WE'LL MAKE A PREEMPTIVE STRIKE OF OUR OWN...

?!!

...YOU'RE GONNA HAVE TO HANG OUT IN THAT TREE FOR TEN BILLION SECONDS!!

UNTIL THE DEADLY GAS GETS BLOWN AWAY...

HOW WOULD HE GO AND MAKE SOMETHING LIKE THAT IN THIS STONE WORLD?

DO WE EVEN KNOW FOR SURE IF THE GAS IS TOXIC?

WHAT DOES HE THINK WE ARE, STUPID? TEN BILLION SECONDS, REALLY?

HOW LUCKY FOR YOU MORONS.

THIS WILL BE THE FIRST JOB YOU'VE DONE RIGHT.

HUH?

A FAIR POINT, SO LET'S DO THIS RIGHT.

NO SENSE IN RETURNING BEFORE A THOROUGH TESTING OF THIS GAS!

WHOOSH

HEH HEH HEH... IT'S TOTALLY IMPARTIAL.

NATURE'S NOT AN ENEMY OR AN ALLY.

AND YOU'RE THE MORONS WHO MADE A SUICIDE RUN AGAINST THE KINGDOM OF SCIENCE AND ITS MODERN WEAPONRY.

BETTER RUN HOME AND ASK MAMA TSUKASA FOR SOME MILK!

YOU BET I DID...

YOU COOK THIS UP, STRING BEAN?!

TOXIC GAS?

YOU'RE OKAY. THE TOXIC GAS WON'T GET THIS HIGH!

AHHHHH!

KERFWOOSH

...WIND.

DEADLY...

FWUMP

...I'VE GOT A GOOD FEELING ABOUT THIS...

CAN'T SAY...

THIS RUNT'S MAKING US WORK FOR IT!

Huff

Huff

WE SHOULD BREAK ONE OF HER LEGS ONCE WE CATCH HER...

WHOOSH

?

WHOOSH

SHE SAID SHE WAS HEADING FOR THE HOT SPRINGS MOUNTAINS ...

I COULDN'T STOP HER!

WHERE DID SUIKA GO?!

...

DRAW THEM AWAY FROM THE KINGDOM.

RUN AND HIDE. RUN AND HIDE.

THE DANGER'S YET TO COME.

ISN'T THIS THE HOT SPRING AREA?

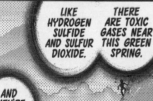

LIKE HYDROGEN SULFIDE AND SULFUR DIOXIDE.

THERE ARE TOXIC GASES NEAR THIS GREEN SPRING.

AND THEY'RE HEAVIER THAN AIR.

INTENSE WIND COMING DOWN OFF THE MOUNTAIN!

AND SO THEY CAN'T SET MORE FIRES TO SMOKE SUIKA OUT...

...SUIKA WILL RUN UPWIND.

UP INTO THE MOUN- TAINS!

I APPRECIATE HER SIMPLENESS ...

HOW NOBLE... SACRIFICING HERSELF AS BAIT TO PROTECT THE OTHERS.

AND THAT WILL BE FAR EASIER THAN ATTACKING THE SCIENCE WARRIORS ON THEIR HOME TURF.

...BECAUSE CATCHING THAT CHILD MEANS VICTORY.

SHF

...BUT SUIKA'S GONNA PROTECT THE KINGDOM OF SCIENCE!!

SUIKA MIGHT BE LITTLE...

POP!

GET HER!!

THIS DUMB KID WAS TOO SLOW TO GET AWAY!

BWA HA HA! CHECK IT OUT!

TP TP TP TP TP TP

WE HAVE NO CHOICE BUT TO KEEP THEM SAFE IN THE STOREHOUSE!!

HOW CAN WE PROTECT THEM ALL ON OUR OWN?!

FNOOM

?!!

FLIK

CHROME SPENT YEARS BUILDING UP THAT STOCKPILE, AND MONTHS OF OUR HARD WORK WENT INTO THE REST OF THE LAB!

IF WE LOSE ALL THAT...

NOOOO! IT'S ALL GOING UP IN SMOKE!

WATER!!

BAD NEWS. NOW THAT THE FIRE'S STARTED...

...THE WIND COMING DOWN OFF THE MOUNTAIN'LL FAN THE FLAMES.

IT'S A WIND OF DEATH!

THE HOUSES ARE BURNING DOWN, TOO!!

EVERYONE EVACUATE!!

MWA HA HA! NOW WE JUST GOTTA NAB ONE OF THE BRATS THAT'S BEEN SMOKED OUT.

WITH A HOSTAGE, IT'LL BE OUR WIN!!

THAT'S RIGHT!

...WE SAW THAT THIS SENTIMENTAL BUNCH WOULDN'T ABANDON A SINGLE SENTRY.

LAST TIME, DURING OUR FIRST SKIRMISH...

OOM

FIRE!!

OH CRAP!!

AND YET, IF ONLY YOU'D NOTICED...

...THAT OUR LITTLE BATTLE WAS A MERE DIVERSION...

...YOU MIGHT'VE DONE EVEN BETTER.

Z=49: To the Present

I EVEN SET THE STAGE RIGHT.

YOU SEE, HOUND'S BERRY IS MY FAVORITE FLOWER.

FOR IN FLOWER SYMBOLISM...

...IT MEANS "LIAR."

SHUP

SHF

HOUND'S BERRY...

THIS STRANGE SUN PLANT BLOOMS BEST IN THE SHADE.

ZZZ
ZZZ
ZZZ

WOOF!

WOOF!

SENKU WOULD NOTICE FOR SURE, AS GOOD WITH THE NATURAL SCIENCES AS HE IS.

AND SINCE SUIKA SPENT HER DAYS PLAYING AMONG THE FLOWERS OF THE FOREST...

...SHE RECOGNIZED IT INSTANTLY.

THAT MAGICIAN'S GOT ALL SORTS OF STUFF UP HIS SLEEVES.

PIPE SPEAR? OH, BECAUSE OF THIS BIT OF BAMBOO THAT'S ATTACHED?

ERIOUSLY-SAY?!

WHO WOULD DO SUCH A THING?!

IT WAS MADE ESPECIALLY HARD TO DETECT...

A STONE TOOL COULD NEVER MAKE THAT CLEAN OF A CUT THROUGH THE STRAP.

...SO THAT THE SPEAR WOULD FALL APART WHEN FORCE WAS APPLIED...

A BRILLIANT BIT OF TRICKERY.

NOT BAD AT ALL, LITTLE GEN!

YOU DIRTY, TRAITOROUS TURNCOAT!

YOU'VE REALLY DONE RIGHT.

WHY WOULD YOU SAY SUCH HURTFUL THINGS...?

WHATEVER DO YOU MEAN, DEAR HYOGA?!

THE POINT
OF THE
SPEAR
JUST...

...FELL
APART
ON ITS
OWN...

CAN'T KEEP TRACK OF...

...THE SPEAR TIP!

THIS TECHNIQUE IS UNIQUE TO THE KAN RYU STYLE.

THE TWISTING BY HIS RIGHT HAND IS AMPLIFIED, WITH THE PIPE AS A FULCRUM.

THIS ALLOWS THE SPEAR TIP TO TRACE A FULL CIRCLE.

I'M DEAD...

THOUGH THAT MUCH IS PLENTY OBVIOUS.

I APPRECIATE THE TIP, GEN.

POP

THE VILLAGE'S THREE STRONGEST ARE MAGMA, KOHAKU AND KINRO!

TAKE THEM DOWN NOW, AND IT'S OUR WIN, HYOGA!

NO, HE'S SENDING US A SECRET MESSAGE...

OUR ONLY HOPE OF WINNING IS FOR ALL THREE OF US TO RUSH THE ENEMY AT ONCE!

HE'S GONE AND TRIPLE-CROSSED US!

WHAT AN OPPORTUNIST!

IS THAT GEN JERK OUR ENEMY TOO?!

MWAHHHHH!!

WERE YOU EVEN LISTENING?!

ZOOSH

THAT'S OUR MAGMA...

EEP! MIND ASKING FIRST?

SHP

GIMME THAT!

THE SPEAR USER NAMED HYOGA...

...IS THE REAL THREAT HERE.

HIS AURA IS ON ANOTHER LEVEL!

SPLASH

FWOO

OoooooOM

Z=48:
Blades of Science

YOU'LL KNOW IT'S READY WHEN THE FIRE TURNS PURPLE.

CHARCOAL FROM PINE CAN REACH 1,200 DEGREES.

COULD IT BE A KATANA OR SOMETHING?

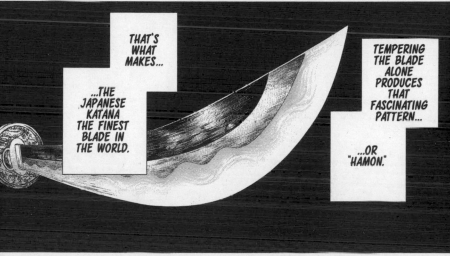

THAT'S WHAT MAKES...

...THE JAPANESE KATANA THE FINEST BLADE IN THE WORLD.

TEMPERING THE BLADE ALONE PRODUCES THAT FASCINATING PATTERN...

...OR "HAMON."

THE FINISHING TOUCHES MIGHT BE A LITTLE OFF, BUT...

GO ON. KEEP THE PRAISE COMING.

YOU'VE DONE RIGHT, HERE...

EXQUISITE.

...KINGDOM OF SCIENCE.

GETTING EXCITED ABOUT CRAFTING PUMPS UP HIS MUSCLES...

INTENSE...

...WIND COMING DOWN OFF THE MOUNTAIN!

...TO WORK HARD!!

WE NEED ALL OF ISHIGAMI VILLAGE...

BUT NOW IT'S TIME.

YUP. SOMETHING THAT GEN WAS REAL EAGER TO HAVE US MAKE, THOUGH HE WAS JUMPING THE GUN.

HM? HE WANTED SOMETHING SPECIFIC??

THE MAN IN THE BLACK MASK SEEMED TO BE A SKILLED WARRIOR.

DO YOU HAVE A SCIENTIFIC STRATEGY TO BEAT HIM?!

HOO BOY!

KRIK KRIK

SOUNDS GOOD TO ME...!!

KRIK

PUFF   PUFF

CH AK

SORCERY IS AWESOME... I MEAN, SCIENCE!!

SO KINRO'S FUZZY-EYE DISEASE IS CURED?

OH HHH

Oh my... Oh my...

BAAAD! AND SUPER-COOL!

OUR SCIENTIFIC WAR PLANNING DOESN'T END HERE!

NO GETTING LAZY, NOW! IT'S A RACE TO BE READY BEFORE THE NEXT STORM COMES!

SUIKA JUST FEELS RIGHT AT HOME IN A GOOD HELMET!

OH, YOU TOO, SUIKA! YOU'VE GOT A NEW HELMET!

SWIP

SWIP

AND IF THEY'RE KILLED IN BATTLE...

...I'LL LEARN EVERY LAST TRICK UP THE KINGDOM OF SCIENCE'S SLEEVE.

AFTER ALL, THESE FOOLS WERE MADE TO BE DISPOSABLE PAWNS.

CHIRP

CHIRP

...YOU'RE JUST ANOTHER STRING BEAN WHO COULDN'T PUT UP A FIGHT.

WITHOUT THAT PIPE SPEAR, OR WHATEVER YOU CALL IT...

HAH!

YOU'RE SCARED, AIN'T YOU, HYOGA?!

!!

APOLO-GIES, DEAR HYOGA.

OH! BECAUSE OF THIS BIT OF BAMBOO THAT'S ATTACHED?

PIPE SPEAR...?

UNLESS YOU WANT TO DIE, I WOULD ADVISE PUTTING THAT DOWN.

SHOULD THEY WIN, ALL WILL BE WELL.

HM... WITH THEM SO EAGER TO CHARGE INTO BATTLE...

...PERHAPS SENDING THEM AGAINST SENKU AGAIN COULD WORK.

...

IF THOSE STRING BEANS DIDN'T HAVE GUNS, I WOULDA...

BEAN STRING

GAHHHH!

WE CAN'T GO CRAWLING BACK TO TSUKASA AFTER GETTING OUR BUTTS HANDED TO US!!

THEY'RE WARY OF OUR IMAGINARY GUNS, AND THEY'LL PROBABLY HANG BACK UNTIL THE WEATHER TURNS.

GENTLY GUIDE THEM TO THAT DECISION, GEN.

...DURING A STORM, WHEN THEIR FIREARM FUSES WILL BE UNUSABLE.

SO WE OUGHT TO ATTACK...

I'M GOOD AS NEW!

BAAAD!!

TMP

TMP

HE'S NOT ALL GOOD!!

TREMBLE TREMBLE TREMBLE

HANG ON... IT'S JUST A TOUGH-GUY ACT!!

WELL, NOT NECESSARILY.

WE CAN PREDICT WHEN THEY'LL SHOW UP AGAIN!

...WILL COME AND ATTACK AGAIN!

WE HAVE NO IDEA WHEN THAT GANG FROM YESTERDAY...

AS A SENTRY, I CAN'T VERY WELL BE BEDRIDDEN.

THAT'S KINRO... DEDICATED TO THE END.

HOW CAN YOU BE SO DEDICATED?!

I HAD TO MAKE SOME OF THIS WHILE CREATING OUR SULFONAMIDE PANACEA.

ACETANILIDE. FEVER REDUCER AND ANALGESIC.

THE ONE THAT EXPLODED.

E=mc²

Eeesshh

NOOO! KINRO'S DEAAAAD! Wahhhhh!

I-I'M STILL ALIVE...

DON'T KILL ME OFF YET, GINRO.

TOMORROW?!

SOUNDS TOO GOOD TO BE TRUE...

TAKE SOME OF THIS! JUST CRAM SOME SULFONAMIDES INTO YOUR WOUND...

...AND TOMORROW YOU'LL BE GOOD AS NEW!

FWOMP

GUH?

Z=47: Science vs. Power

Kohaku

Power	☆☆☆
Speed	☆☆☆☆☆
Technique	☆☆☆
Reach	☆☆

Kinro

Power	☆☆☆
Speed	☆☆
Technique	☆☆☆
Reach	☆☆☆☆☆

Hyoga

Power	☆☆☆
Speed	☆☆☆☆☆
Technique	☆☆☆☆☆
Reach	☆☆☆☆☆

Magma

Power	☆☆☆☆☆
Speed	☆☆
Technique	☆
Reach	☆☆☆

IF WE'RE TALKING RAW POWER, THAT'D BE MAGMA FOR SURE.

??

WHO'S THE BURLIEST DUDE HERE?

THROW THIS STONE AT THE ENEMY...

...AS HARD AS YOU CAN!

MY DEAR MAGMA.

HUH??

HOW WILL THAT WORK IF THE ENTIRE VILLAGE IS LOST?

STAND UP AND FIGHT.

DON'T YOU...

...WANNA STEAL THE CHIEF'S THRONE FROM SENKU?

AND WHY SHOULD I LISTEN TO A WORD YOU SAY?!

I'LL NEVER HIT 'EM WITH THIS!

IT'S FINE IF YOU MISS.

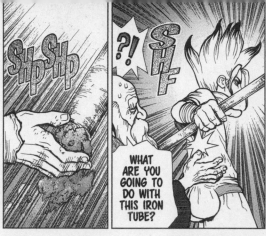

SlipSlip

?!

SHF

WHAT ARE YOU GOING TO DO WITH THIS IRON TUBE?

I NEVER THOUGHT I'D USE IT AS A BLUFF, OF ALL THINGS.

HEH HEH HEH... I'M GLAD I SAVED SOME GUNPOWDER.

IF IT COMES DOWN TO IT, THIS LAST BIT OF GUNPOWDER MIGHT SAVE THE DAY.

UHHH...

!

ERIOUSLY-SAY...?

SHZZZ

ARGHH... BROKE...
...MY NOSE...

S-SORRY, HYOGA.

THESE SO-CALLED PRIMITIVES KNOW THEIR STUFF.

YOU THOUGHT YOU STOOD A CHANCE WITH A SWORD...

...AGAINST A SPEAR WIELDER ON A NARROW PATH? HAVE YOUR BRAINS TURNED TO MUSH?

KRAK

SHAH

CELEBRATION

CHILDREN'S AREA

KINRO

ENEMIES

GINRO...

...CUT THE BRIDGE DOWN WITH ME ON IT.

IF I'M KILLED...

TMP

IF THEY REACH THE CHILDREN'S AREA, IT'S ALL OVER.

YOU SCARED, YOU PRIMITIVE PUNK?!

THIS ONE'S READY TO RUN!

SHUP

!

HE'S QUITE IMPRESSIVE.

HE INSTANTLY REALIZED HE'S AT A NUMBERS DISADVANTAGE...

...SO HE'S DRAWING MY PEOPLE INTO ONE-ON-ONE CONFRONTATIONS ON THE BRIDGE.

GUARDING THE VILLAGE IS OUR DUTY!

SHOULD THEY ATTACK NOW, THE CELEBRATION WOULD BE THE LEAST OF OUR CONCERNS...

...WITH A STUBBORN JERK WHO CAN ONLY SAY "RULES ARE RULES."

I WANNA PARTY TOO...

INSTEAD I'M STUCK HERE...

BY BLOWING INTO THIS HERE STICK.

THAT'S RIGHT! I MADE THAT.

HUH?

ABOUT WHAT...?

GINRO... HURRY. ALERT THE OTHERS!

SHAH

IF ONE OF THEM IS LEADING THE WAR PARTY...

...AND HYOGA, WHO WAS REVIVED RECENTLY.

BUT THE MOST DANGEROUS ONES ARE TSUKASA...

ALL OF YOU!

YOUR ONLY OPTION IS TO FLEE...

IT'S FINALLY TIME FOR THE BATTLE BETWEEN THE KINGDOM OF SCIENCE AND THE BRUTE-FORCE EMPIRE!

IT'S ALL-OUT WAR!

GEN. IT'S NOT LIKE YOU SAW SENKU'S CORPSE.

IF, AGAINST ALL ODDS, HE'S ALIVE...

...WE'LL TAKE THAT VILLAGE BY FORCE.

AS SOON AS MY WARRIORS ARE READY...

...HE MIGHT FIND THAT VILLAGE ONE DAY AND BUILD HIS KINGDOM OF SCIENCE.

INDEED... THAT WOULD BE THE WORST-CASE SCENARIO.

THAT'S THE LONG AND SHORT OF IT. HE'S BEEN DEPETRIFYING THEM LIKE MAD.

YOU'RE TELLING US THAT THE LONG-HAIRED MAN...

...HAS AN ENTIRE ARMY OF PEOPLE AS ABSURDLY STRONG AS HE IS?! AND THEY'RE ON THEIR WAY HERE?!

Z=46: Stone Wars

Z=45: Epilogue of Part 1 (End of Part 1)

Part 2: Stone Wars

BOOM
BOOM

BOOM
BOOM

BOOM

NOW THAT THE VILLAGE HAS COME TOGETHER, I'D BETTER TELL HIM...

BESIDES, I NEED MY WITS ABOUT ME TO MAKE MY DEADLY SERIOUS REPORT.

Cola?

NO THANK YOU... I'M STRICTLY A COLA MAN.

WHAT'S HAPPENED ...

OH YEAH? TELL ME WHAT, MENTALIST?

...IN THE TSUKASA EMPIRE?

THE VILLAGE GRAVEYARD.

...WAS BROUGHT HERE, ON BEHALF OF OUR FOUNDERS.

THIS SMALL GRAVE MARKER...

EVEN IF IT'S TRUE, THERE'S NOT SO MUCH AS A PINKIE BONE LEFT DOWN THERE.

HEH HEH HEH... THEY DIED 3,700-ODD YEARS AGO.

OKAY.

I'LL HEAD BACK TO THE VILLAGE.

I'M GONNA...

...DO SOME RESEARCH HERE.

THE 100 TALES...

HAVING TROUBLE DOING IT IN ENGLISH, THOUGH...

GO WITH JAPANESE THEN. I'D LOVE TO LEARN YOUR MOTHER TONGUE.

I FIGURED IT'D BE MORE FUN IN STORY FORM.

JUST SOME ESSENTIAL KNOWLEDGE TO HELP OUR DESCENDANTS SURVIVE.

WRITING A STORY??

I'D EXPECT NO LESS FROM A FORMER PROFESSOR.

ASTRONAUTS

United States

Lillian Weinberg

Former Job: Singer

A diva with worldwide fame. Her spirit for adventure led her to purchase a tourist seat on the Soyuz rocket.

Japan

Byakuya Ishigami

Former Job: Professor

A romantic at heart with a goofy side. His leadership qualities made him the right man to rally the other astronauts.

United States

Connie Lee

Former Job: NASA Employee

Married Shamil while on the deserted island. The couple was ready to forgo tradition, but Byakuya egged them on.

Russia

Shamil Volkov

Former Job: Pilot

The polar opposite of Byakuya, Shamil tends to put emotion aside and make logical decisions. Captain of the Soyuz rocket. His hobby is chess.

Russia

Darya Nikitina

Former Job: Doctor

She's got a sharp tongue, but a kind heart. She gives Yakov a lot of guff, though they actually get along quite well.

Russia

Yakov Nikitin

Former Job: Doctor

The only one on the ISS staying for a second time. He's meeker than he looks, but his research skills are unparalleled.

OR WHAT WAS LEFT OF HIM.

...THE HARD TRUTH...WE WERE THE LAST OF HUMANITY.

...HAD TO ACCEPT...

THAT WAS WHEN WE SIX...

WE ALSO HAD THE RECLUSE'S FACILITIES TO WORK WITH.

LIFE ON THE ISLAND WASN'T THAT BAD.

ASTRONAUTS UNDERGO SURVIVAL TRAINING FOR JUST SUCH A CHALLENGE.

THE SURVIVAL KITS BUILT INTO THE SOYUZ CRAFTS...

TA-DAHHH!

FWEEE EE

8
9
217,510
SECONDS.
1
2

SIXTY HOURS...

...AFTER HUMANITY TURNED TO STONE...

WHOOOSH

Z=44: One Hundred Nights,
One Thousand Skies

CONTENTS

6

STONE WARS

Dr.STONE

STORY

Every human on Earth is turned to stone by a mysterious phenomenon, including high school student Taiju. Nearly 3,700 years later, Taiju awakens and finds his friend Senku, who revived a bit earlier. Together, they vow to restore civilization, but Tsukasa, once considered the strongest high schooler alive, nearly kills Senku in order to put a stop to his scientific plans.

After being secretly revived by his friends, Senku arrives at a village and wins the villagers' trust thanks to his scientific knowledge. According to one of the village's legends, an astronaut named Byakuya started this tribe. Byakuya also happens to be Senku's father!

Byakuya and his colleagues were not petrified while out in space, so when they returned, they decided to try to save humanity. Byakuya also left a message behind for his son, trusting that one day he'd find it...

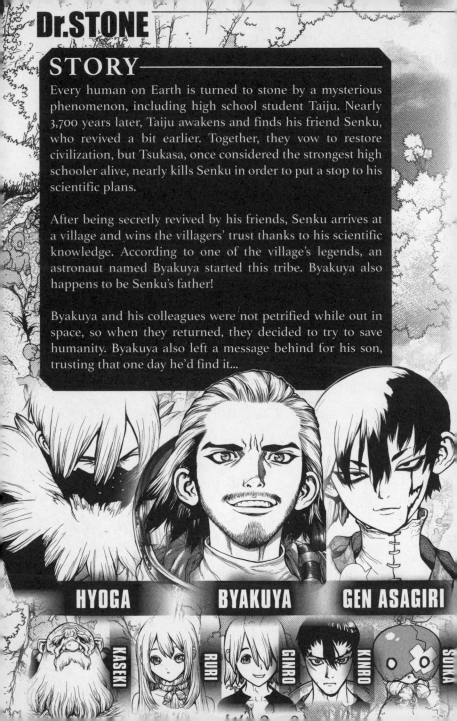

HYOGA   BYAKUYA   GEN ASAGIRI

KASEKI   RURI   GINRO   KINRO   SUIKA

CHARACTERS

KOHAKU

An experienced, agile warrior who's as strong as any man. She's quite possibly the strongest person in the village.

CHROME

A clever and honest guy with more curiosity than he knowns what to do with. Now that Senku's opened his eyes to science, he's ready to go as far as that path takes him.

SENKU

A young man with prodigious knowledge and a passion for science. He's now leading his Kingdom of Science. His catchphrase is "Get excited!"

E=mc²

6

STONE WARS

Dr.STONE

STORY **RIICHIRO INAGAKI**
ART **BOICHI**

Dr. STONE

6

SHONEN JUMP Manga Edition

Story RIICHIRO INAGAKI
Art BOICHI

Translation/**CALEB COOK**
Touch-Up Art & Lettering/**STEPHEN DUTRO**
Design/**JULIAN [JR] ROBINSON**
Editor/**JOHN BAE**
Science Consultant/**KURARE**

Consulted Works:
• Asari, Yoshito, *Uchu e Ikitakute Ekitainenryo Rocket wo DIY Shite Mita (Gakken Rigaku Sensho)*, Gakken Plus, 2013
• Dartnell, Lewis, *The Knowledge: How to Rebuild Civilization in the Aftermath of a Cataclysm*, translated by Erika Togo, Kawade Shobo Shinsha, 2015
• Davies, Barry, *The Complete SAS Survival Manual*, translated by Yoshito Takigawa, Toyo Shorin, 2001
• Kazama, Rinpei, *Shinboken Techo (Definitive Edition)*, Shufu to Seikatsu Sha, 2016
• McNab, Chris, *Special Forces Survival Guide*, translated by Atsuko Sumi, Hara Shobo, 2016
• Olsen, Larry Dean, *Outdoor Survival Skills*, translated by Katsuji Tani, A&F, 2014
• Weisman, Alan, *The World Without Us*, translated by Shinobu Onizawa, Hayakawa Publishing, 2009
• Wiseman, John, *SAS Survival Handbook, Revised Edition*, translated by Kazuhiro Takahashi and Hitoshi Tomokiyo, Namiki Shobo, 2009

Published by VIZ Media, LLC
P.O. Box 77010
San Francisco, CA 94107

10 9 8 7 6 5 4 3 2 1
First printing, July 2019

viz.com

shonenjump.com

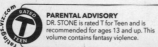

BOICHI

For chapters 42–44, I used over 1,070 reference photos. It was brutal work for several weeks, but my staff and I poured our hearts into it. Why? I have special feelings for the Soyuz rockets and Baikonur base since one of my past series was set in Russia. In order to learn about the country's history, literature, food and mafia, I read Russian books, listened to Russian music and even tried cooking Russian food. After all, I know that I need to cultivate a certain love for a culture if I want to portray it. With that series, I tried to convey Russia's passion, loneliness and solemnity.

In a way, doing this part of *Dr. Stone* revived my passion for Russia. I still haven't traveled there in person, but I hope to someday!

RIICHIRO INAGAKI

I visited a spear dojo for research!

This picture's small and it's hard to tell, but the spear on the left is blurry. The "pipe spear" has the spear itself going through a pipe, and just like Hyoga's, it spins around. There's no blocking that!

They even let me try it out. I got it to spin just fine, but pulling off an actual attack was another story. I need more training!

Boichi is a Korean-born artist currently living and working in Japan. His previous works include *Sun-Ken Rock* and *Terra Formars Asimov*.

Riichiro Inagaki is a Japanese manga writer from Tokyo. He is the writer for the sports manga series *Eyeshield 21*, which was serialized in *Weekly Shonen Jump*.